Cool Clive and the Bubble Trouble

MICHAELA MORGAN

Illustrated by Dee Shulman

OXFORD
UNIVERSITY PRESS

OXFORD
UNIVERSITY PRESS

Great Clarendon Street, Oxford OX2 6DP

Oxford University Press is a department of the University of Oxford.
It furthers the University's objective of excellence in research, scholarship,
and education by publishing worldwide in

Oxford   New York

Auckland   Cape Town   Dar es Salaam   Hong Kong   Karachi
Kuala Lumpur   Madrid   Melbourne   Mexico City   Nairobi
New Delhi   Shanghai   Taipei   Toronto

With offices in

Argentina   Austria   Brazil   Chile   Czech Republic   France   Greece
Guatemala   Hungary   Italy   Japan   Poland   Portugal   Singapore
South Korea   Switzerland   Thailand   Turkey   Ukraine   Vietnam

Oxford is a registered trade mark of Oxford University Press
in the UK and in certain other countries

British Library Cataloguing in Publication Data
Data available

ISBN-13: 978-0-19-919993-8
ISBN-10: 0-19-919993-0

1 3 5 7 9 10 8 6 4 2

Available in packs
Stage 12 More Stories C Pack of 6:
ISBN-13: 978-0-19-919991-4; ISBN-10: 0-19-919991-4
Stage 12 More Stories C Class Pack:
ISBN-13: 978-0-19-919998-3; ISBN-10: 0-19-919998-1
Guided Reading Cards also available:
ISBN-13: 978-0-19-918375-3; ISBN-10: 0-19-918375-9

Cover artwork by Dee Schulman
Photograph of Michaela Morgan © Richard Drewe

Printed in China by Imago

Chapter 1

Wherever Jade goes ...

...trouble follows.

She's mad.

She's mad about animals.

She's always coming home with animals.

She's come home with injured birds,

stray cats,

even dogs.

Once she came home with the
school hamster.

'I didn't want it to be lonely in
school by itself,' she said.

She's a bit more sensible now.

But not a lot.

She's still mad about animals.
She watches Pet Rescue every week
and every week she says:

And every week Mum says:

Every Saturday, Jade drags me and my mum to the pet shop to look in the window and to talk to the pet shop people. They know us well now.

Jade makes notes which she uses when she tries to persuade Mum to let us have a pet.

But Mum always says the same thing.

Chapter 2

So, just before the school holidays, when Miss Strictly asked:

Can anyone look after Bubble, the school hamster, in the holidays?

I knew exactly what Jade would do. I could imagine it. She would jump up and down, wave…and scream…and cry…and beg …and embarrass me.

I had to stop her. Quickly! I crept forward.

'scuse me–

THWACK

Oops

sorry!

All this time, Miss Strictly was still talking.

Looking after a
pet is a big
responsibility...

... a pet is
not a toy...

... you can't
just leave it and go
on your holidays.

On and on she went
and on and on I crept,
getting nearer
and nearer to Jade.
I could see she was
about to burst.
I had to stop her!

blah... only those who are keen, careful...blah...

It isn't easy to get from my row in the Juniors, up to Jade's row in the Infants, but I had nearly made it when...

Ohhhhh!

SKID

'Well, Clive!' said Miss Strictly.

You certainly ARE keen! Let me think ...

You are one of the biggest kids now... You always try your best...

... and I KNOW you can keep your cool.

'So, as long as your mum agrees, you *can* look after Bubble in the holidays.'

YIPPPEEE!!

So then I had to persuade Mum.

I asked Mum
to write a letter
to Miss Strictly.

4 Jubilee Road

Friday 23rd July

Dear Miss Strictly

Clive and Jade have my
permission to have
Bubble to stay with us
for the holidays.

Yours sincerely,
Bella Wallace

Miss Strictly gave
me the hamster,

the cage,

the food,

and a lot of instructions.

INSTRUCTIONS

1 Keep bowl filled
   with food.
2 Keep bottle filled
   with fresh water.
3 Keep fresh sawdust
   in cage.
4 Clean cage every week.

I tried to listen carefully to Miss Strictly, but it was a bit hard with Jade jumping up and down asking:

I started to wonder and worry.

But I knew that Bubble was never any trouble at school.

Nothing could go wrong.

Could it?

Chapter 3

We took the hamster home and we set
her up in my bedroom.

'She will be safer with you, Clive,'
said my mum. 'But you can visit her
whenever you want,' she said to Jade.

All that day I had
Bubble in my room.
So, of course, I had
Jade in my room too.

All day she was there in my room, playing with my things and talking to the hamster.

What a pest.

She dressed all my Action Men up wrong.

She messed with my Lego.

She drew on one of my posters.

All the time she kept asking:

What a pest!

But although Jade was a bit of trouble,
Bubble was no trouble at all.
Bubble just lay
there curled up
and snoozing.
No trouble
at all.

Until ...
much later that night, when I put out
the light and settled down to sleep.

You know that lovely moment when
you start to drift into a dream?
I was just drifting when ...

...Bubble woke up.

Bubble got busy collecting food

and

Bubble was shovelling food from here to there...

and from there to here...

and back again.

That was only the beginning.

There was the whirring around the wheel…

the swinging from the cage bars…

and the splashing in the water bowl…

What a night!

Chapter 4

'Can Jade have the hamster in *her* room tonight?' I asked.

'Can I? Can I?' Jade joined in.

In the end, Mum gave in.

Yes...all right... I suppose so.

That's when the real trouble began.
Jade wouldn't leave Bubble alone.
She kept waking that poor hamster up.

Now you know what it feels like to be kept awake.

Jade kept playing with Bubble.
She kept putting the hamster:

in toy cars...

vroom!

swoop!

and aeroplanes...

Wheee!

and giving her rides
and slides...

Pretty Bubble!

and dressing her up.

I think Bubble was
getting a bit fed up.

Anyway, in the end even
Jade got tired and Bubble
was put back in her cage.

'Did Bubble keep you awake all
night?' I asked Jade the next morning.

'No, she was as quiet as … a mouse,'
said Jade. 'No trouble at all.'

'Funny!' I thought. 'Maybe you tired
her out during the day. Let's have a
look...Oh...'

Bubble had disappeared…

vanished …
  escaped …
    vamoosed …
      split …
        quit …
          packed up …
            moved off …
            moved on.

She had gone!

Chapter 5

We looked everywhere.

Under the bed...

in the cupboards...

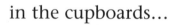

in the toy box.

But there was no sign of Bubble.

No sign at all.

Mum will go mad, Jade thought.

The teachers will go mad.

All the other children will go mad.

And Bubble will be sad.

'Don't worry,' I said. 'We'll find her.'

But as the hours went by

and the day went by

and the night went by,
there was still no Bubble.

asked Mum.

'She's very quiet,' said Mum.

'Where is she?' asked Mum.

Not long.

Bring,
Brrrinnnng!

The phone rang.

Oh lovely!

Mum turned to us.
'Some of your friends
from school are coming
to see Bubble tomorrow.
Won't that be lovely?'

Uh oh!

Now what are we
going to do?

Chapter 6

'They'll all hate me. They'll all say it was my fault!' wailed Jade.

She looked up to me as her big brother to have a brilliant idea

and I did!

I took my money from my money box – my holiday money –

and I took Jade down to the pet shop.

'Have you got any brown and white hamsters?' I asked.

We found one that looked like Bubble – but a bit fatter. Jade called it Ghost of Bubble because it looked just like her, and we bought it.

Everyone said the new Bubble was looking well.

'They're looking after her very well,' said my mum.

Everything was fine. Well, *nearly* everything was fine.

Jade was still worried about the real Bubble.

So, on Friday when
Jade poured out
her cornflakes

...and Bubble
landed in the
bowl,

Jade was very happy indeed!

Bubble was looking very well.
Well fed and fat. It must have been all
those cornflakes she'd been eating.
    We popped her in the cage with
Ghost of Bubble.
    'Brilliant!' said Jade.

Everything's perfect!

Chapter 7

Everything was *not* perfect. We had two hamsters now instead of one.

I had hardly any holiday money left.

Worst of all, Bubble and Ghost of Bubble didn't seem to get on. They were always biting and fighting, tussling and scuffling.

We took what was left
of my holiday money

and all of Jade's
money and went
back to the pet shop.

We popped Bubble or Ghost of Bubble
in to the new cage.

So now the problem was solved – except Jade had no money. I had no money. And we had *two* hamsters and *two* cages to explain to Mum.

We stuffed one of the cages under a towel and hoped Mum wouldn't notice.

How long do you think we can get away with this?

Not long.

One morning, we pulled back the towel and what did we find?

Looking just like tiny sausages, there they lay:

tiny baby hamsters.

'What's all this?' said Mum. So then we had to tell her.

Now we've got no money,

two cages,

and ten hamsters.

'It's a nightmare!'
I said.

'It's a disaster!'
my mum said.

It's a
hamster hotel!

'DING!'

Then I had another idea!

I took Jade
and I took my mum
and we went back
to the pet shop.

'Yes,' said the pet shop
man, wearily.

'You sell hamsters
don't you?' I asked.

'Yes,' said the man, warily.

'Do you buy animals
too?' I asked.
'Because we've got
…a few spare hamsters.'

Then we told him all about it. 'Hmm …' said the man.

'People are always asking for hamsters, so I suppose I *could* buy them.

'BUT I don't want the adults – just the youngsters – and I don't want *any* of them for a few weeks.'

So we kept them all for a few weeks.
Every day at about the same time
they would all wake up and go

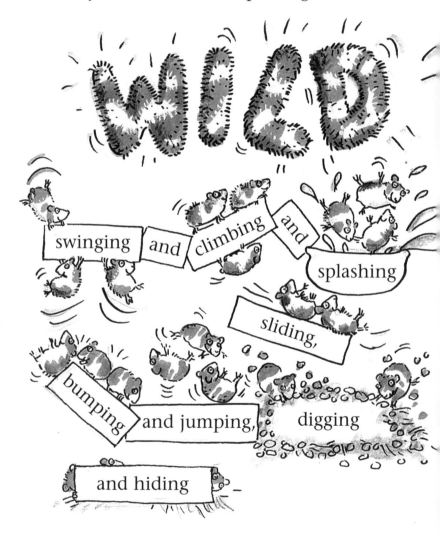

WILD

swinging and climbing and splashing

sliding,

bumping and jumping, digging

and hiding

nosediving ...

bellyflopping

and
just
going

"bonkers"

I call it

Hamster Mania!

It's all working out brilliantly.
We've sold the baby hamsters,
so the baby hamsters will get good
homes – and we will get some holiday
money.

Most important of all,
Bubble is safe and ready
to go back to school.

Everything is perfect now, except…

There's just one problem left.

'Do you mean me?' asked Jade.

'No,' I said. 'I mean the baby hamsters have all got homes and Bubble is going back to school, but *we've* still got a spare grown-up hamster

and a cage.

Jade looked worried.

Mum looked thoughtful and then …

'I suppose we could keep her,' said Mum. 'If you really want to.'

So we did.

Jade BEAMED for weeks. She'd learned her lesson and now treated animals with proper respect.

Jade's Pet rules

1. Shut cage door properly.

2. Remember to feed pets.

3. Don't dress them in dolly clothes.

I made sure she never forgot about the time our house turned into a hamster hotel.

About the author

This is my fourth story about Clive. He is like a real person to me. I can imagine what he'd like, what he'd say, what other adventures he could have.

I have had some similar experiences to Clive. I, too, had a hamster – and it escaped. I bought a replacement and... it escaped. I ended up with lots of baby hamsters and guess what? They escaped.

I think I should try for a pet that cannot squeeze out of a hamster cage.

An elephant perhaps?